CONTENTS

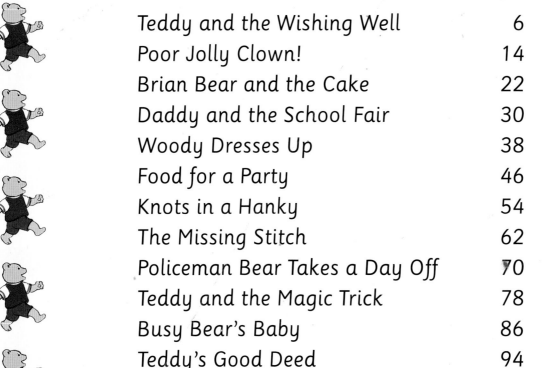

First Published 2000 by Brown Watson
The Old Mill, 76 Fleckney Road,
Kibworth Beauchamp, Leics LE8 0HG

ISBN: 978-0-7097-1343-2

NOW I CAN READ

15 Two Minute Tales

Stories by Maureen Spurgeon
Illustrations by Jenny Press

Brown Watson
ENGLAND

TEDDY AND THE WISHING WELL

It had been hot for a long time in Teddy Town. 'We have hardly any water!' said Policeman Bear.

'No water?' said Teddy. 'But what about our paddling pool?'

'What about my crops?' said Farmer Bear. 'I have even used up the water in my old well!'

'A well,' Teddy said to himself. 'Just the thing!' He found some bricks and set to work.

'Hello, Teddy!' called Barry Bear. 'What are you doing?'

'Making a well,' said Teddy.

'You need cement,' said Barry. 'I will go and fetch some.'

By the time he came back, Teddy had set the bricks in a circle on the ground.

'Well done!' smiled Barry.

They stuck the bricks together. Then they fixed sticks at the side of the well and tied a bucket on a rope.

'You cannot get water from that well, Teddy!' cried Policeman Bear, laughing.

'A well must be sunk deep into the earth to draw water from the ground!'

'It can be a wishing well,' said Teacher Bear. 'Let us wish!'

Nobody said what they wished, but next day, Farmer Bear's crops grew fresh and green and birds splashed in a puddle. There was even water in the wishing well! Everyone agreed, rain was needed just as much as sunshine.

'And we got our wish, Barry!' cried Teddy. 'Well, well!'

READ THESE WORDS AGAIN!

water   paddling

crops   bricks

cement   circle

fixed   sticks

laughing   earth

ground   nobody

splashed   sunshine

WHAT CAN YOU SEE HERE?

Teddy

puddle

Policeman
Bear

Farmer Bear

wishing well

POOR JOLLY CLOWN!

Bella Bear was very upset.

'Look at Jolly Clown!' she said to Teddy. 'I lost him in the park! By the time Busy Bear found him, he was like this!'

Poor Jolly Clown! His hair had come out and his face was faded. Even his jolly smile had gone.

'Let us go and see Toy-Mender Bear!' said Teddy. 'He can make toys as good as new!'

'Poor Jolly Clown!' said Toy-Mender Bear. 'I shall do my best to fix him.'

Next day Bella told Teddy, 'I cannot wait any longer. I want to go and see Toy-Mender today! I must see if Jolly is better!'

When they got to Toy-Mender Bear's workshop, the door was open.

'I cannot mend this old thing!' he was saying. 'See his broken face? His paint is worn. His hands are crooked. I was going to put him in the bin!'

'You cannot put Jolly Clown in the bin!' yelled Bella loudly. 'If you cannot mend him, I shall take him home with me!'

'Who said I cannot mend Jolly Clown?' asked Toy-Mender Bear. 'I was telling Clock-Mender Bear about my old grandfather clock! Jolly is much better!' he added. 'He can go home tomorrow!'

Bella looked at Jolly Clown. His paint gleamed. His eyes shone. His smile was as wide as ever.

'Thank you, Toy-Mender Bear!' she said.

And, even the grandfather clock seemed to wink.

READ THESE WORDS AGAIN!

upset	found
hair	faded
smile	broken
face	worn
crooked	tomorrow
gleamed	eyes
smile	even

WHAT CAN YOU SEE HERE?

Bella Bear

Jolly Clown

Toy-Mender
Bear

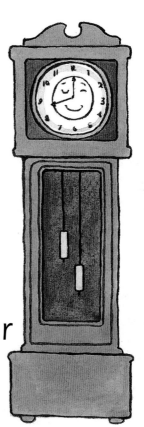

grandfather
clock

Clock-Mender Bear

BRIAN BEAR AND THE CAKE

Brian Bear had made a big cake to share with his friends. 'It looks a bit plain to me,' he told Teddy.

'We can make some icing,' said Teddy. 'And chocolate spread!'

Brian went to fetch the things from the kitchen. On the wall was a picture of Bella with Jolly Clown. 'A clown cake!' he cried. 'That is an idea!'

He began cutting bits off the cake. An oblong for the body and a round shape for the head!

Then a bit to make a hat! He rolled out some marzipan to make hair for the clown and Teddy made a marzipan jacket.

'He can have chocolate boots,' said Brian, 'chocolate eyes, a chocolate nose and a big icing sugar smile! What a cake!'

'It is a bit small, now,' said Teddy, 'and we made too much marzipan and chocolate spread.'

Just then, there was a ring at the door. There was no time to make anything else!

'Brian!' cried Bella. 'You and Teddy HAVE been busy!'

'All these lovely little cakes!' said Teena. She tasted a piece that had been cut off.

'Mmm..! Try a marzipan dip!' said Woody. He put some on his bit of cake. 'Scrummy!'

'And this chocolate dip!' said Billy. 'Mmmm, yummy!'

'What about our clown cake?' asked Brian.

'That looks lovely!' said Teena. 'MUCH too good to eat!'

READ THESE WORDS AGAIN!

cake	friends
chocolate	spread
kitchen	clown
oblong	round
shape	hair
sugar	anything
piece	lovely

28

WHAT CAN YOU SEE HERE?

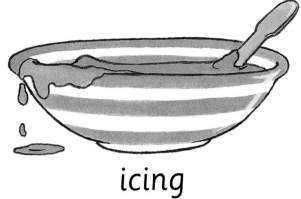

marzipan

icing

jacket

picture

boots

DADDY AND THE SCHOOL FAIR

There was going to be a School Fair to raise money for some new toys. What ideas everyone had!

'Skittles!' said Teddy Bear.

'Coconut shy!' said Bella Bear.

'Egg and spoon races!' cried Billy Bear. 'And lucky dips!'

Teddy told Mummy Bear all about it. 'Good idea!' she said. 'We can make cakes to sell!'

Daddy Bear took off his reading glasses. 'You also buy too many things at school fairs!' he said.

'I do NOT!' said Mummy. 'You spend money, too!'

Daddy shut his book. 'I help in other ways!' he said. 'Teddy, help me pack some books to sell!'

Lots of bears came to the Fair. 'I must buy some cakes,' said Mummy.

'But, Mummy,' said Teddy, 'WE made lots of cakes to sell!'

'Yes,' she said, 'but I like the cakes baked by Baker Bear!'

Suddenly Daddy Bear gave a shout, and rushed over to the book stall.

'I left my glasses in that box of books by mistake!' he told Teacher Bear. 'Here they are, inside this book!'

'If you want that book,' said Teacher Bear, 'you must buy it!'

'Yes, yes!' said Daddy. He was glad to have his glasses back! 'We must raise money for the school!'

'Fancy buying your own book, Daddy!' smiled Teddy. 'I wonder what you are going to buy next?'

'Ice creams!' said Daddy. 'I wonder who wants one?'

READ THESE WORDS AGAIN!

fair	raise
money	new
toys	ideas
reading	glasses
other	suddenly
shout	rushed
inside	wonder

WHAT CAN YOU SEE HERE?

skittles

coconut shy

books

lucky dip

ice cream

WOODY DRESSES UP

Woody was putting up lots of fairy lights at Bear Towers, ready for Lady Bear's garden party.

'What fun, Lady Bear!' Teena was saying. 'Will you tell Woody?'

'No need!' said Lady Bear. 'He always looks the same!'

Woody looked down at his old clothes. 'Yes,' he told himself. 'I must look smart for the party!'

On the way home, he saw an old top hat in Brian's dustbin. 'Woody!' cried Brian. 'Can I borrow your tie?'

'Yes!' said Woody. 'Can I have this top hat?'

'Take it!' said Brian.

Then Woody saw a scarf on Farmer Bear's scarecrow! 'Woody!' cried Farmer. 'Can I borrow your jacket?'

'Yes!' said Woody. 'Can I have this scarf?'

'Take it!' said Farmer Bear.

Grandpa was throwing away an old suit. 'Woody!' he cried 'Can I borrow your hat?'

'Yes!' said Woody. 'Can I have that old suit?'

'Take it!' said Grandpa.

The day of the party arrived.

'Woody!' cried Lady Bear. 'You do look smart in your suit, your scarf and your top hat!'

Woody just stared. Brian wore Woody's tie. Farmer Bear wore Woody's jacket. Grandpa wore Woody's old hat!

'It is a tramps' fancy dress party!' giggled Teddy. 'You are the smartest bear here, Woody!'

Everyone started to laugh, even Woody. They all had a wonderful party!

READ THESE WORDS AGAIN!

garden	party
lady	looked
old	dustbin
tie	scarf
borrow	jacket
throwing	smart
fancy	giggled

WHAT CAN YOU SEE HERE?

fairy lights

clothes

top hat

scarecrow

suit

FOOD FOR A PARTY

Teena Bear was having a party at Honeypot Cottage! Teddy had helped Daddy to make cheese rolls. 'Here comes Wood-Cutter Bear!' cried Daddy. 'We can take all these on his handcart!'

'Do not forget my milk shakes!' said Mummy. She fetched some big jugs, each with a lid on top.

Soon, they met Gardener Bear. She was bringing lots of salad.

'Lovely!' said Teddy. 'I LOVE salad sandwiches!'

Next, they met Baker Bear. She had made cakes and jam tarts for the party. Wood-Cutter Bear put them all on his cart.

'Let us call for Woody!' he said. But when they reached Woody's caravan, all was quiet.

'Ssh!' said Woody. 'See those rabbits? I think they are lost! And I have no food for them!'

'What about some salad?' said Gardener Bear. She took some from the cart.

Just then, some squirrels appeared.

'They look hungry to me!' said Teddy. 'Do they like cheese rolls?'

'Give some cake to these poor gulls!' said Baker Bear. 'When they fly inland, it is because there is bad weather at sea!'

When they got to Honeypot Cottage, Teena was at the gate.

'I AM glad to see you, Mummy Bear!' she cried. 'Can you spare some milk shake for this kitten?'

Teena did not understand why everyone began to smile!

READ THESE WORDS AGAIN!

party	cheese
helped	rolls
salad	sandwiches
cart	quiet
reached	gardener
hungry	there
bad	weather

WHAT CAN YOU SEE HERE?

rabbits

squirrels

cottage

gulls

kitten

KNOTS IN A HANKY

Binky Bear had a habit of forgetting! He had a bath and forgot the soap! He went swimming and forgot his towel!

Then Teddy had an idea. 'Tie a knot in your hanky, Binky!' he said. 'Then you will not forget!'

Binky had forgotten his hanky, but there was one in his desk that he had forgotten about! 'What must I not forget?' he asked.

'Sports Day, tomorrow!' said Teacher Bear. So Binky tied a knot in his hanky.

'You are playing cricket!' said Teddy. 'Do not forget your bat!'

So Binky tied another knot. 'A knot for Sports Day and a knot for a bat!' he said

'And a ball!' added Billy.

So Binky tied another knot in his hanky! 'A knot for Sports Day, a knot for a bat and a knot for a ball!' he said.

'And do not forget to bring a packed lunch!' said Teacher.

So Binky tied another knot. 'A knot for Sports Day, a knot for a bat, a knot for a ball.'

'And don't forget a knot for your packed lunch!' said Teddy

The knots in his hanky helped Binky to remember all the things he needed for Sports Day! And his knotted hanky? That made a fine sun-hat to stop his head from getting burnt!

'Clever Binky!' smiled Teddy.

'No I am not!' said Binky. 'You told me to tie knots in my hanky so that I would not forget!'

'But it was you who did not forget to tie the knots!' said Teddy.

READ THESE WORDS AGAIN!

habit	forgetting
swimming	idea
knot	hanky
desk	sports
tomorrow	another
needed	things
remember	clever

WHAT CAN YOU SEE HERE?

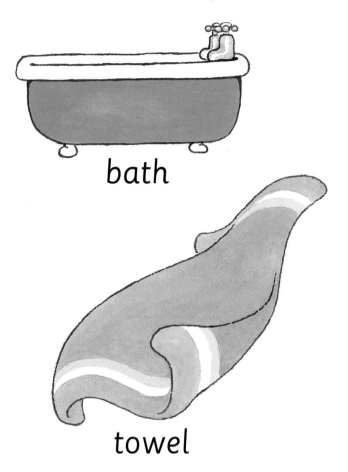

bath

towel

bat

packed lunch

knotted hanky

THE MISSING STITCH

Kitty Bear never stopped knitting!

'What are you knitting, now?' asked Teddy.

'Socks and a scarf for Woody!' she said. 'Oh, I have dropped a stitch!'

'Where did she drop it, Teddy?' asked Billy. 'Did you see?'

'No,' said Teddy. 'We must see if we can find another one!'

Woody was in his garden.

'Ooh!' he gasped, rubbing his side. 'I have got a stitch!'

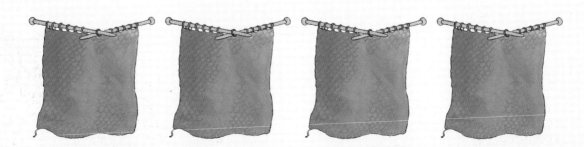

'A stitch?' cried Teddy. 'Is it the one Kitty Bear dropped?' But Woody had already gone indoors.

'So much mending!' somebody else was saying. 'All these things will need a lot of stitching!'

'Busy Bear!' cried Teddy. 'Woody had a stitch just now!'

'Woody?' said Busy Bear. 'Well, I did try to mend his pullover! But as fast as I stitched, the old stitches came undone...'

'We only need ONE stitch!' cried Billy Bear, pulling at the pullover.

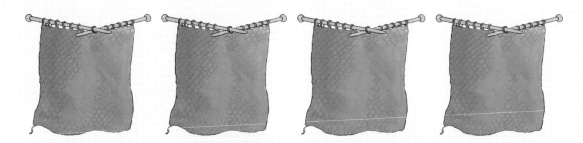

One stitch came undone. Then another and another. They ran back to Kitty with lots of undone stitches!

'Here is your stitch, Kitty!' said Teddy. 'The one you dropped!'

'I did drop a stitch,' said Kitty, 'but I soon picked it up again!'

Teddy and Billy looked at each other. It did not make sense!

'All this wool!' Kitty went on. 'I can make the scarf I was knitting into a pullover for Woody!'

But Teddy and Billy never did find out about the dropped stitch!

READ THESE WORDS AGAIN!

never asked

dropped stitch

gasped rubbing

already indoors

mending undone

pulling another

picked looked

each sense

WHAT CAN YOU SEE HERE?

knitting

socks

garden

pullover

wool

69

POLICEMAN BEAR TAKES A DAY OFF

'Policeman Bear needs a day off!' said Teddy.

'He works hard!' agreed Barry.

'But who can take over?' said Binky. 'Think hard!'

A loud voice made them jump!

'Farmer!' cried Busy Bear. 'Your tractor is blocking the road!'

Farmer Bear looked a bit cross. But he soon moved his tractor!

'Thank you, Busy!' said Woody. 'I was waiting to cross!'

Then Busy saw Billy and Bella. They were playing ball. 'Hey, you two!' she cried. 'It is not safe to play near the road. Come to the park with me and Baby Bear.'

Teddy, Barry and Binky looked at each other. Then they followed Busy Bear to the park.

'We have a job for you!' said Teddy.

'A job?' cried Busy Bear. 'Oh, I DO like being busy!'

She also liked the idea of Policeman Bear taking a day off. So they all went to see him!

'You need a day off!' said Teddy firmly. 'Busy is taking over!'

'Grandpa Bear has invited you to tea!' said Busy. 'Off you go!'

Well! Policeman Bear DID enjoy his day off. And Busy enjoyed walking around, checking doors and windows and seeing bears across the road!

Now, Policeman Bear likes having a day off! And everyone likes to see him having a rest.

And, Busy Bear?

'I just like being busy!' she says.

74

READ THESE WORDS AGAIN!

off	over
voice	busy
road	cross
two	park
job	idea
invited	tea
enjoyed	walking
around	across

WHAT CAN YOU SEE HERE?

tractor

Busy Bear

ball

door

window

TEDDY AND THE MAGIC TRICK

Everyone loved Magic Bear in his cloak and top hat. 'Close your hand!' he told Teddy. 'Now, I will tap your elbow with my wand and say – Hold Tight! All Right!'

Teddy opened his hand and there he found a bright, shiny coin!

'Again, I will tap your elbow with my wand!' said Magic Bear. 'Hold Tight! All Right! Now the coin has gone behind your ear! It is yours to keep, Teddy!'

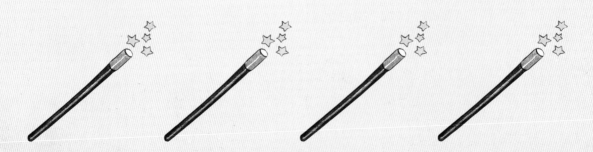

Teddy wanted to do some magic! He found a stick for a wand and a raincoat with a hood.

'I will hold my coin,' he cried, 'tap my wand and say – Hold Tight! All Right!' The coin was still in his hand!

'Some trick!' said Bella. 'Magic Bear tapped your elbow!'

So Teddy bent his arm right up.

'I tap my elbow with my wand,' he said, 'and say – Hold Tight! All Right!'

By mistake, he dropped the coin into the hood! So, when he held out his hand, it was empty!

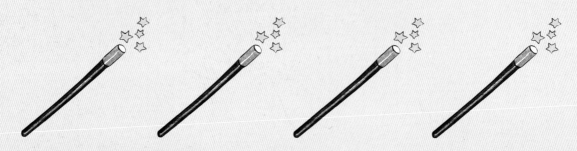

'You made the coin disappear!' said Billy. 'Now get it back!'

'I tap my elbow with my wand,' said Teddy, 'and I say – Hold Tight! All Right!' Teddy took the coin from inside his hood, then held out his hand to show them all.

'Do it again!' cried Barry.

So Teddy dropped the coin into his hood and showed them his empty hand. Then he bent his arm and took the coin out again! Nobody knew how he did it, not even Magic Bear!

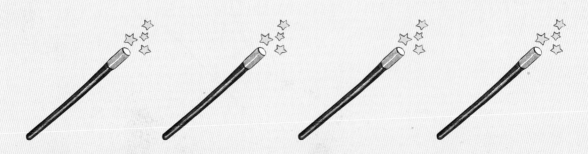

READ THESE WORDS AGAIN!

magic	everyone
tight	right
ear	shiny
stick	mistake
dropped	empty
disappear	trick
inside	again

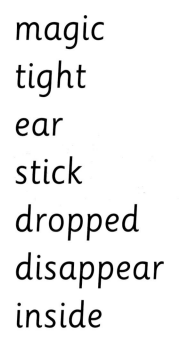

WHAT CAN YOU SEE HERE?

a bright coin

cloak

magic wand

raincoat

elbow

BUSY BEAR'S BABY

Busy Bear liked being busy. She also liked telling everyone what to do and how to do it!

'It is no use weeding when the sun is out!' she told Daddy Bear.

'That is quite the WRONG way to hold a cricket bat!' she told Teddy. 'You will never hit the ball like that. Let ME show you how to do it properly!'

'That Busy Bear!' moaned Daddy.

'That Busy Bear!' groaned Teddy.

'That Busy Bear!' said Mummy. 'She is putting her baby in a Baby Show! It is all she talks about!'

It was true. 'My baby MUST win the Baby Show,' Busy Bear kept saying. 'Then I shall have a party!'

Busy Bear cleaned her house, ready for the party! She even painted the flowerpots on her windowsill!

Soon it was time to get Baby ready. When she lifted him up, Busy Bear screamed!

'My baby has red spots on his face!' she cried. 'Is it Measles?'

'Heat rash!' said Mummy Bear. 'Or it could be chicken pox.'

'Send for the doctor right away!' said another bear.

Teddy felt something drip on his head. He looked up.

'It is paint!' he cried. 'Red paint!'

Busy Bear stroked Baby's chin. 'Teddy is right!' she said, looking up at the flowerpots, then looking at her baby again. 'No Baby Show for you, baby!' she said at last. 'You need a nice bath, instead!'

READ THESE WORDS AGAIN!

quite	wrong
groaned	moaned
show	true
kept	cleaned
house	ready
screamed	right
nice	instead

WHAT CAN YOU SEE HERE?

baby

face

paint

flowerpots

windowsill

93

TEDDY'S GOOD DEED

It was Good Deed Day in Teddy Town. First, Teddy saw Grumpy Bear trying to cross the square. 'It is Good Deed Day, Grumpy!' he cried. 'Let me take you across the square!'

'I do not WANT to go across the square!' cried Grumpy Bear. 'I was waiting for the bus!'

'Sorry,' said Teddy. Just then, Baby Bear threw a doll out of her pram! Teddy picked it up.

'It is Good Deed Day, Baby!' he said 'So, here is your doll!'

'Good deed?' said Busy Bear. 'I wanted her to throw that away!'

Teddy nearly bumped into Teena, carrying lots of shopping.

'It is Good Deed Day!' he said. 'Let me carry your shopping!'

'No, Teddy!' cried Teena. She had to run after him. 'I was only looking after Woody's shopping! Now I must carry it back!'

The next bear Teddy saw was Toy-Mender Bear, leaning on a stick!

'Poor Toy-Mender!' cried Teddy. 'Here, take my arm...'

'No!' shouted Toy-Mender Bear.

But it was too late! There was a loud CRACK and the stick broke!

'I was holding that stick for the glue to set,' said Toy-Mender Bear.

Poor Teddy!

'I only wanted to do a good deed!' he said, sadly.

'Good deed?' cried Grumpy. 'That IS a joke!'

Grumpy Bear began laughing so much that everyone forgot to be cross! Making him laugh really was the best good deed of the day!

READ THESE WORDS AGAIN!

good	deed
trying	cross
square	picked
wanted	bumped
carrying	next
crack	stick
laugh	forgot

WHAT CAN YOU SEE HERE?

bus

doll

pram

shopping

glue

TEDDY AND GRIZZLE BEAR

'Grizzle Bear,' said Teddy, 'is ALWAYS grizzling at school!'

'Boo-hoo!' Grizzle grizzled, all day long. 'I want to go home!'

'If only she smiled!' said Teacher Bear. 'She might forget to grizzle!'

'Let us try!' said Teddy. 'I am tired of Grizzle grizzling!'

Billy Bear put on a funny mask.

'Go away!' Grizzle grizzled.

Barry Bear tried to give her a balloon. 'Boo-hoo!' Grizzle grizzled. 'It may go bang!'

'Let us look in the toy box!' said Teddy at last. 'Come on!'

Still grizzling, Grizzle took out a toy. 'I dropped my hanky in the toy box!' she grizzled. 'Boo-hoo!'

Teddy put his hand inside. He could not reach. He leaned over the top. Still he could not reach. He leaned a bit more, and – bump! Teddy fell inside!

Somehow, he stood up, with the box over his head.

'Ha-ha!' giggled Grizzle Bear. 'Funny Teddy Bear!'

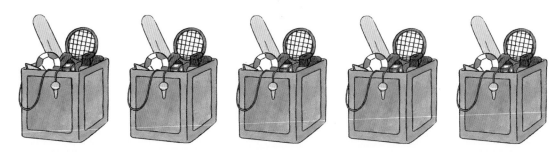

Teacher helped Teddy out of the box. Grizzle was giggling so much, all the class giggled too!

'So, Teddy made you smile, Grizzle!' smiled Teacher Bear. 'Do you want to go home now?'

'No!' said Grizzle. 'Do some more funny things, Teddy!'

'Not now!' smiled Teacher. 'It is time for a story!'

Teddy was pleased about that. Making Grizzle smile had been very hard work!

READ THESE WORDS AGAIN!

grizzle	try
tired	away
toy	bang
come	still
could	bump
helped	giggled
story	work

WHAT CAN YOU SEE HERE?

funny mask

balloon

toy box

Grizzle
Bear

Teacher
Bear

TEDDY AND THE SCHOOL PLAY

'We are having a school play!' said Teddy.

'How nice!' said Mummy. 'What part are you playing?'

'That is a secret!' said Teddy. 'Toy-Mender Bear is making my costume!' He said no more.

'I hear Teddy is in the school play!' said Baker Bear. 'Is he busy learning all his words?'

'No,' said Mummy. 'So, he cannot have anything to say.'

'All Teddy told ME,' said Teena, 'was that he had to make noises!'

'Noises?' said Baker Bear.

'Nothing to say?' said Mummy.

'Toy-Mender Bear making his costume?' said Daddy.

Policeman Bear frowned. 'I must look into this,' he said.

Everyone came to the play! Bella was the queen, Billy, the king, Barbara, the princess, Binky, the miller's son, and Barry, the crafty old wizard.

Then, someone else appeared!

It was someone in a furry black costume with pointed ears, fine whiskers, a long tail and a very loud 'PURR!' and 'MEOW!'

'Puss in Boots!' someone cried.

They all cheered! Clever Puss in Boots, the magic cat who helped the miller's son to beat the wizard and marry the princess!

But the best part was when Puss took off the mask which Toy-Mender Bear had made.

'Teddy!' everyone cheered as they saw his face. 'Good old Teddy Bear!'

READ THESE WORDS AGAIN!

school	play
secret	busy
words	anything
noises	frowned
everyone	king
queen	furry
purr	boots
cheered	face

WHAT CAN YOU SEE HERE?

costume

princess

Puss in Boots

wizard

mask

PRESENTS FOR CHRISTMAS

Teddy Town is very busy at Christmas time! Wood-Cutter Bear cuts lots of Christmas trees. Baker Bear bakes lots of cakes. Then there are presents to give!

'Teddy, please take a Christmas pudding to Grandpa Bear,' said Mummy. 'Billy can go with you!'

Billy and Teddy liked Grandpa. They went to his little house and Teddy knocked at the door.

'Here is a present for you, Grandpa!' said Teddy.

Grandpa smiled. But he sounded sad. 'I wish I had a present for you, Teddy,' he said.

Teddy did not know what to say. He turned away. Teena was across the road, looking all around.

'What do you want?' he called.

'Holly,' said Teena. 'But I cannot find any over here.'

'Plenty in my garden!' smiled Grandpa. 'Help yourself!'

Teena was pleased. She liked holly!

'Take all you like!' said Grandpa. 'My holly bushes need cutting!'

Teddy and Billy had an idea! They helped Grandpa to write a notice and tied it to the gate.

TO ALL MY FRIENDS.
HELP YOURSELVES TO HOLLY.
MERRY CHRISTMAS FROM
GRANDPA BEAR.

So many bears came to see Grandpa that Teddy and Billy had to help pick the holly!

'Merry Christmas, Grandpa Bear!' said Teena. And everybody joined in. 'Merry Christmas! Merry Christmas!'

READ THESE WORDS AGAIN!

Christmas	time
presents	trees
house	knocked
smiled	sounded
around	garden
bushes	idea
notice	tied
everybody	joined

WHAT CAN YOU SEE HERE?

Baker Bear

Christmas tree

Christmas pudding

holly

gate